ALSO AVAILABLE IN PAN

Impressionist

Elementarist

Fauvist

Surrealist

HISTORIC DISCOVERIES IN THE WORLD OF ART

We have already seen how and why art was invented, and it is illuminating to follow its development over the centuries. Willie's influence here cannot be disputed. What else could account for the quite unnecessary displays of nudity among statues, frescoes and paintings? The Venus de Milo, for instance, would have looked much more comfortable in a nice warm cloak, and it would have hidden her unfortunate accident. But no. She, like hundreds of other unfortunate girls, was made to strip for posterity.

Botticelli, Rodin, Rubens, Picasso – they were all at it, spurred on by what they liked to describe as the creative muse. Artists got away with behaviour that would have had more conventional men like bank managers thrown into jail. And yet the theory that Willie was behind every great work of art is not strictly accurate. He was usually in front.

An extraordinary collection of what could be called partial self-portraits has recently been discovered which illustrates in graphic fashion the significant changes in artistic technique. Here we see Willie as never before. Heaven knows what this lot would fetch at Sotheby's.

PRE-TELEPHONE ROMANCE

Dear Mary
I love thee dearly.
Perchance we may have
a tryst some eventide in
the lee of the olde barn at
Melchester. I prithee hasten
thy reply since none of us
is getting any younger.
Your ever loving
William

TWO WEEKS LATER..

Dear William
I am sorry but I
fear my heart belongs
to another.
kind regards
Mary

A whole fortnight wasted!
Gotta do something..

SO WILLIE HAD ONE OF HIS SLAVES INVENT THE PHONE, AND NOW:

Hi Mary. My body is available tonight. Wanna meet up?

Not a chance

Ok - try Jane

THE HORSELESS CARRIAGE:

AND SO...

THE WHEEL:

ELECTRICITY:

It was a dark night.
The candle was out.
Static was in the air.
On a sudden wild
impulse Thomas Edison
pulled down his
girl friend's panties.
They sparked (and
they weren't even nylon)
Willie was shocked.
Edison was intrigued.
So he did it a few
more times.....

Hello!

From there, gentlemen, it was but a few short experiments to my greatest idea — the electric light bulb!

Yeah — but pulling down her panties was my idea.

INVENTIONS and how they happened.
Where do ideas come from?

HERE

AND
HERE

All inventions start out as a silly question. They are also born of necessity. And that necessity usually has its root somewhere south of the brain.

DOCTOR LIVINGSTONE. African explorer and missionary, he tried to eradicate racial predjudice before anyone had even heard of it — as in his classic meeting with American journalist Henry Stanley:

Well you presume wrong — I'm M'boto. Dr Livingstone is the one with the spear.

One day him bwana sense of humour gonna get him in big trouble.

So — its true what they say..

I'm afraid so, old thing

5 The South Seas

Prompted by the sight of a welcoming committee dressed in grass skirts, visiting industrialists from Birmingham invented the lawnmower.

6 Hong Kong and Singapore

Strategically placed within striking distance of the riches of the Orient and small but perfectly formed young women in *cheongsam* dresses.

THE GOLDEN AGE OF THE BRITISH EMPIRE

Most historians would agree that Britain was at her most powerful and influential during the reign of Queen Victoria, from 1837–1901, when it was said that the sun would never set on the British Empire. Gentlemen adventurers voyaged to the ends of the earth, planting the Union Jack all over the place and bringing civilization to savage and untamed peoples.

Noble work, you might say, but what was behind this great exodus from Britain? What was so attractive about foreign parts in those days? We do not have to look far for the answer: it was Victorian society, which insisted that all women should look as much like bell-tents as possible. Bustles and crinolines and upholstery covered the female population, and the result of this was that Victorian Willie had to leave the country to see a broad. It is no accident that the most popular spots were those where feminine fashions had a certain informality, as can be seen quite clearly from the accompanying map and footnotes.

1   Africa

What with the heat and the absence of shopping centres, most African ladies were obliged to walk around in oversized handkerchiefs. This inspired many men to give up promising military careers and join the missionary movement.

2   India

Home of the clinging *sari* and the famous temple carvings depicting the 174 positions which lead to perfect bliss (providing that cramp or dislocation do not interfere with the proceedings). It is not surprising that the British lingered in India until 1945.

3   The Middle East

The Victorians' reaction to belly dancing was never formally recorded. The only clue that exists is a cryptic postcard sent home by an eminent sociologist: 'I have discovered the secret of the Sphinx's inscrutable smile.'

4   The West Indies

The British introduced cricket to the islands. The islands introduced the British to rum and limbo dancing. This may explain why our cricket is in such a bad way today.

THE NIGHT THAT ENDED IN A BANG

It had all been so carefully worked out. Guy Fawkes had rented a cellar under the Houses of Parliament and, posing as a pregnant MP, had managed to smuggle thirty-six barrels of gunpowder in under his cloak. All he had to do was make the bangers, light the blue touch-paper and retire.

But as he was crouched in the cellar one night, wondering whether to make a couple of extra rockets and a Giant Whizzer, just to be on the safe side, he heard a knock at the door. Ye gods, he thought to himself, I am undone. 'Tis the Old Bill for sure.

Imagine his surprise when the door opened and young Nell, the office cleaner, came in with her feather duster and phone-sterilizing kit. A comely wench with a saucy twinkle in her eye, it wasn't long before she had persuaded Guy Fawkes to show her his Jumping Jacks. One thing led to another, and then the little hussy wanted to see his Roman Candle, and all thoughts of blowing up Parliament were forgotten.

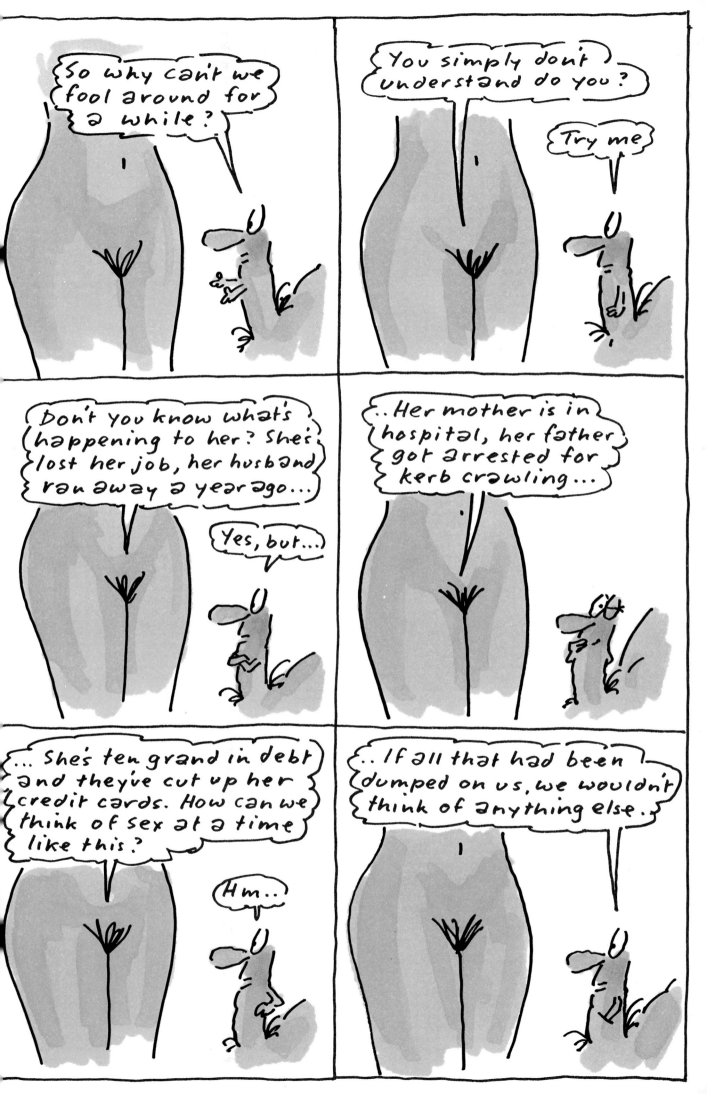

Nine out of ten answered, 'Yes, and the more they do it the better.' (A typically crude response that could only have come from one source.) The signatures mounted up, and were duly presented to the Honourable Members in Westminster. What else could they do in the face of such overwhelming pressure from the man in the street but give women the vote?

THE WOMEN'S MOVEMENT

It is strange that of all the social advances that have taken place since history began, this one owes more to the intervention of the original male chauvinist than any other. It was also the first time that a public opinion poll was used for political purposes. It happened more or less like this.

The Suffragettes had been having no luck at all, mainly because people thought they were yet another pop group, with an act built round a lead singer who chained herself to railings. After years of effort, the best they had been able to manage was an offer to open the show at the Empire, Leicester Square.

It was decided to try something completely different. Posing as market research executives, the Suffragettes roamed the length and breadth of London seeking signatures for a petition. Men were stopped on the street and asked: Are you in favour of the Women's Movement?

WISECRACKS THAT CAUSE ALIMONY:

ALIMONY IN SIMPLE TERMS

THE INVENTION OF ALIMONY

Kings and persons of great power and importance have always been much more badly behaved than the rest of us because they have more opportunities. The royal Willie, with unlimited access to ladies-in-waiting, can be guaranteed to make a beast of himself, and usually gets away with it. The case of Henry VIII, however, led to painful results, one of which is still with us today.

Henry's way with the ladies was simple: courtship was followed by marriage, and marriage was followed by execution, which was so much quicker than a long-drawn-out divorce.

Alas for Henry, people started to talk. The royal Press Secretary was pestered by reporters, and there were rumblings of discontent in the Hampton Court branch of the Women's Institute. To make matters worse, Henry was feeling restless with his third wife, and wanted to be rid of her.

'Off with her head!' said Henry.

His advisers were horrified, but the queen wouldn't agree to a divorce. The wisest men in the kingdom were summoned to consider the matter. Eventually a decision was reached, and a spokesman went to see the king.

'I have found the answer to your problem, sire', said the adviser. 'It is passing expensive, but I think the queen may go for it.'

Henry brighted up at once. 'What's the deal?, he asked.

'It is called alimony, my liege.'

SIR ALEXANDER FLEMING

WILLIAM SHAKESPEARE was a klutz with women. But with inspiration from the other 'Willie' he compensated for this by writing brilliant plays. Hamlet's famous soliloquy came almost entirely from below.

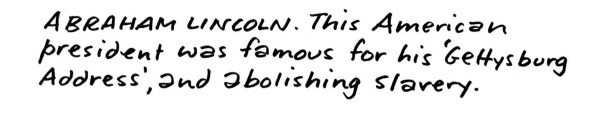

ABRAHAM LINCOLN. This American
president was famous for his 'Gettysburg
Address', and abolishing slavery.

CUSTER'S LAST-BUT-ONE STAND. GENERAL CUSTER once said 'Life is what happens to a man while he's making other plans'. Unfortunately he wasn't listening at the time.

CASANOVA

No matter how busy, tired or seriously injured he was, women were always running through his mind.

OLIVER CROMWELL could have had more fun, but was too aggressive and stupid to spot a racing certainty

WICKED WILLIE'S HALL OF FAME

We all need our heroes, and Willie is no exception. As you would expect, his heroes are not the kind of people you would want to take home to mother, but they make up an interesting cross-section of some of the most upstanding characters in history.

William the Conqueror

It's the name here, rather than the man, as this is how Willie tends to think of himself. Close inspection of the Bayeux Tapestry reveals the original Willie the Conqueror dressed in chain mail and steel helmet. No wonder he looks cross.

Sir Lancelot

The champion, in his day, of mixed jousting, it was he who inspired those famous words from Queen Guinevere: 'What a knight!'

Sheikh Baby Sheikh

Pioneer of the harem, sometimes known as the king-size Bedouin, he died in his twenties with a smile on his face, leaving 238 widows.

Casanova

The original Man Who Wouldn't Take No For An Answer. In addition (since most of his lady friends had jealous husbands) he perfected various escape techniques, including an astonishing ability to run with his trousers round his ankles.

Guru Swamabindra Ghosh

Literally 'he who bends over backwards in the pursuit of pleasure', Guru Ghosh was the author of the *Kama Sutra*, and the only man in recorded history who made full use of being double-jointed.

RUBENS had a thing about big girls

TOULOUSE LAUTREC was not a small man.
At least, not to the girls who knew him.

As you can imagine, prehistoric Willie refused to take this lying down, but all attemps at the direct approach proved unsuccessful and occasionally very painful. Simply asking a girl to take off her skins was liable to get a man clubbed round the ear.

Aeons went by, and the world population dwindled alarmingly, until one day inspiration came to the rescue. The first creative caveman suggested to a young lady that she might like a picture of herself to fill up that empty space on the wall. Then, as now,

flattery was irresistible, and it wasn't long before she was persuaded to take off first one layer and then the rest. The caveman, whose first attempt this was at the reclining nude, made some scratches on the wall and stood back.

'I don't understand it,' said the girl.

'You're not supposed to,' said the caveman. 'It's art.' And with that he jumped on her.

It still works. Ask any professional photographer.

THE INVENTION OF ART

It's hard to believe now, living as we do in an age of short skirts and low necklines, but the world was once a modest place, similar in many ways to Tunbridge Wells on a slow night.

In the dawn of time, long before page three girls and central heating, everyone dressed to keep out the cold, often wearing several layers of animal skins. Indeed, it was sometimes difficult to tell men apart from women, which led to considerable misunderstanding and embarrassment.

THE FRENCH REVOLUTION

Students may claim that the French Revolution was a reaction against the absolute power of the monarchy, but what really set it off was Marie Antoinette's bosom.

It was a fine bosom, much admired for its symmetry, and one of the nobles in King Louis' court had the idea of making champagne glasses which followed exactly the form of the queenly breast. (In fact, they're still around today – rather like deep saucers on stems.)

Marie was a vain little piece, and was delighted at the thought of her bosom being immortalized in glass. She agreed that the royal glass-blower – a low-born fellow, but skilled in his work – could visit her for a fitting. Her husband the king was equally pleased. A new set of glasses was just the thing to take his mind off the noise that the angry mob was making on the other side of the garden wall.

The day of the fitting arrived, and the glass-blower was ushered into the royal bedchamber. There was Marie, stripped to the waist. The glass-blower warmed his hands and started to measure up, and then the inevitable happened as Willie made a determined effort to join in.

Marie looked down in horror at the intruder.

'Ooooh,' she said, 'these peasants are revolting.'

'*Mon Dieu!*', said her husband the king, 'the revolution! It's here! I'm off.'

Only one other mystery remains unsolved in all the accounts of the French Revolution, and that is the true identity of that master of disguise who called himself the Scarlet Pimpernel. It sounds suspiciously like someone we know.

kiss me, I'll turn into a handsome prince and we'll dance the night away at my palace!
Thanks but I don't like dancing – ask my sister instead

THE INVENTION OF MIXED DANCING

It is only relatively recently that dancing has become a social activity. In ancient times, dances were only held on the following occasions:

1 In preparation for war.

2 To placate the gods following an earthquake or an extended series of power cuts.

3 To encourage rain in times of drought.

4 To amuse the aristocracy.

In every case, dancing was strictly segregated; men danced with men, and women danced with women (a practice that still exists today in the more remote parts of Australia).

Men and women might have gone on like this for ever, except for our friend from the downstairs ballroom, who had a better idea. Instead of jumping up and down waving a spear, surely it would be more fun to jump up and down clutching a woman. Who knows what might develop?

And so it was that men and woman came together on the dance floor, with Wicked Willie in the place of honour.

May we have the pleasure of the next fertility dance?

Not forgetting 'cute'.....

... and 'into':

The discovery of America led to the enrichment of our language with many colourful phrases such as 'Off the Wall' — first used by Mrs. Mark Twain following a bizarre request from her husband.

Words like 'togetherness' appeared, as in :

SIR WALTER RALEIGH first explored the possibility of finding his way into Elizabeth the First's abundant pantaloons. To cool him off she sent him to America. He eventually returned bearing some rather dull gifts.

THE DISCOVERY OF AMERICA

Columbus never set off with the intention of discovering America. The original idea was to go further south and plunder the treasures of the Indies – in other words, to cross the Atlantic and then turn left at America without getting involved in Customs and Immigration formalities, which were appalling even in those days.

But what happened? The transatlantic voyage took weeks longer than expected due to unfavourable winds, and by the time land was sighted on the horizon the sailors were bored stiff. After all, dancing hornpipes with other sailors is no substitute for the real thing.

Despite this, however, the voyage would have gone according to plan had it not been for a single incident which, remarkably, has never been given the importance it deserves.

It took place off the coast of what is now called Long Island. The sun was shining, and from his perch in the crow's nest, the ship's lookout could see signs of movement on the beach. If he had simply shouted 'Turn left' the world would now be a very different place, but instead he suggested that Columbus should take a closer look.

And there, on the beach, were a dozen Red Indian maidens, clad only in beads and feathers, performing (according to which historian you read) either a war dance or an open-air aerobics routine. In any case, the result was the same: Columbus followed his unofficial navigator, who was pointing dead ahead, and forgot all about plundering the Indies the minute that first young lady said 'How?'

ANTONY AND CLEOPATRA

Marcus Antonius was the Rambo of his day. Had Shakespeare not written him some nice lines it's unlikely that he'd have made first base with Cleopatra

started filing past in their diaphonous uniforms. After years of being stuck away in darkest Gaul, it was all too much for him. Under his toga, something stirred, and Titus stayed in the office for three weeks without a break.

Nero was greatly impressed by his nephew's devotion to duty, and all went well until the Feast of Al Dente, the god of pasta, which required several virgins to be sacrificed in between courses. But by then, thanks to Titus,

there were no virgins. All those late nights in the office had been devoted to research and product-testing, and not a single girl remained unresearched.

The gods were furious, and in retribution set fire to Rome. Nero fiddled (as rumour has it, with one of the ex-virgins), and Titus was last seen heading in the direction of a rest home on Lake Como. And that was the beginning of the end of the Roman Empire.

THE DECLINE AND FALL OF THE ROMAN EMPIRE

As a model of discipline and organization, it would be difficult to find a more efficient structure than the Roman Empire in its heyday, even if the men did wear skirts and long dresses.

It was set up along the lines of a modern corporation, with a board of directors (Chairman, Emperor Nero) to oversee vital functions. There was a director in charge of war, rape, pillage and the laying waste of barbarian cities; a Director of Sport and Recreation, responsible for the training of gladiators and the recruitment of Christians and lions; a Director of Social Services, including slaves and eunuchs; a Catering Consultant for feasts (vestiges of which remain to this day in the form of Italian restaurants); an Officer of Public Works, experienced in the erection of triumphal columns; even a dress designer – Marcus Giorgio Armani – for the Emperor's wardrobe.

But of all these administrative posts, none was more important in Roman society than the sacred position of trust which was officially described as Executive Director of Sacrifices and Keeper of the Vestal Virgins.

This was traditionally held by the oldest senator in Rome, a man who could be relied upon to preserve chastity in the girls' dormitory and generally keep his hands to himself. And so for centuries there was a steady supply of sacrificial virgins for those high days in the Roman festive calendar such as August Bank Holiday Monday and Yom Kippur.

Now it came to pass that the Emperor Nero had a young nephew, Titus Lascivious, who was something of a family problem. A nice enough lad, but no Einstein, he had made a terrible mess of governing Gaul, and was clearly not suited to running a country. Also, he was homesick.

Nero took pity on him, and brought him back to Rome. As luck would have it, the oldest senator had just died after a particularly taxing orgy, and Nero gave young Titus the job of looking after the virgins.

The trouble began on his first day in the office. Titus was stock-taking, and the girls

Ye Gods – what happened with the Virgin Claudia last night... .... did .... did we...??

Mind your own business

AMOEBA:

The amoeba is the most primitive life form known. Their sex habits are very basic and they know nothing of disco dancing or sado-masochism. In a way they are very lucky.

The amoeba reproduces by splitting

1   2   3   Congratulations!

Humans split after reproducing

I'm off

Me too

A sad comment on 2,500,000,000 years trying to get it right

DARWIN'S 'Theory of Natural Selection' is a difficult thing to explain. But you can get a rough idea from the Movie Business

Skulking through history, hidden from view by everything from loincloths to the baggiest of designer trousers, is the small but sinister presence who has not only caused more chaos and trouble than Attila the Hun, but has had a wonderful time doing it.

He has never been mentioned by name. There have been vague allusions to something called the Yellow Peril or the Red Menace, and at one time the map of the world was covered in pink blobs (officially, to identify the British Empire), but the little villain has somehow managed to remain anonymous, letting others suffer for his misdeeds.

It has gone on long enough. In the interests of lower education, we shall now tear away the veil of secrecy that has obscured the truth for all these years and expose the guilty party for what he is – the most consistently influential figure in world history.

ARCHIMEDES

A lot of people are taught that the famous 'Archimedes Screw' is a method of making water go uphill

THE MISSING LINK

Learned historians have been scratching their heads and consulting books of reference for hundreds of years in an effort to find some kind of pattern in the development of what we like to call civilization. Why, for instance, was America discovered? What was at the bottom of the French Revolution? Who invented high heels?

Various explanations have been put forward to account for the momentous events that have shaped our destiny. Greed, religion and the eternal nobility of man's spirit have all been blamed at one time or another, but scholarly analysis reveals an altogether different motivating force – the missing link that makes nonsense of all previously held theories.

Some of us believe in Evolution.
Others favour the Adam and Eve story.
It's the right of every human being to
believe in whatever he or she wants.
People have died for this right. Wars
have been fought for it.
So if you happen to believe in the Adam
and Eve nonsense, here's why Adam
often appeared to be talking to himself.